play guitar with
indie rock

HLE

HAL LEONARD EUROPE

Distributed by Music Sales Limited

Published by
Hal Leonard Europe
A Music Sales/Hal Leonard Joint Venture Company
14-15 Berners Street, London W1T 3LJ, UK.

Exclusive Distributors:
MUSIC SALES LIMITED
Distribution Centre, Newmarket Road,
Bury St Edmunds, Suffolk IP33 3YB, UK.

Order No. HLE90004475
ISBN 978-1-78038-380-4
This book © Copyright 2012 Hal Leonard Europe.

Printed in the EU

www.musicsales.com

Edited by Adrian Hopkins
Cover designed by Liz Barrand

AKA...What A Life!
Can't Stand Me Now
Don't Sit Down 'Cause I've Moved Your Chair
Little Lion Man
Sex On Fire
Guitars & Banjo: Arthur Dick
Bass guitar & Double Bass: Paul Townsend
Drums: Noam Lederman

Ruby
Guitars: Arthur Dick
Bass: Paul Townsend
Drums: Brett Morgan
Keyboards: Jonas Persson and Arthur Dick

Run
Guitars, Bass guitar, Keyboards: Tom Fleming
Drums: Dave Cottrell

CD recorded and mixed by Jonas Persson

Your Guarantee of Quality
As publishers, we strive to produce every book
to the highest commercial standards.
The music has been freshly engraved and the book has
been carefully designed to minimise awkward page turns
and to make playing from it a real pleasure.
Particular care has been given to specifying acid-free,
neutral-sized paper made from pulps which have not been
elemental chlorine bleached. This pulp is from farmed
sustainable forests and was produced with special regard
for the environment.
Throughout, the printing and binding have been planned
to ensure a sturdy, attractive publication which should
give years of enjoyment.
If your copy fails to meet our high standards,
please inform us and we will gladly replace it.

guitar tablature explained

Guitar music can be explained in three different ways: on a musical stave, in tablature, and in rhythm slashes.

RHYTHM SLASHES: are written above the stave. Strum chords in the rhythm indicated. Round noteheads indicate single notes.

THE MUSICAL STAVE: shows pitches and rhythms and is divided by lines into bars. Pitches are named after the first seven letters of the alphabet.

TABLATURE: graphically represents the guitar fingerboard. Each horizontal line represents a string, and each number represents a fret.

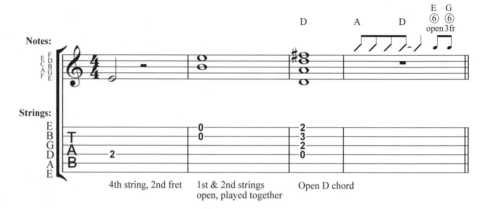

4th string, 2nd fret   1st & 2nd strings open, played together   Open D chord

definitions for special guitar notation

SEMI-TONE BEND: Strike the note and bend up a semi-tone (½ step).

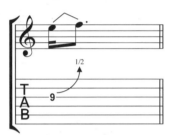

WHOLE-TONE BEND: Strike the note and bend up a whole-tone (full step).

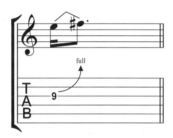

GRACE NOTE BEND: Strike the note and bend as indicated. Play the first note as quickly as possible.

QUARTER-TONE BEND: Strike the note and bend up a ¼ step

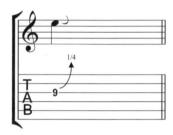

BEND & RELEASE: Strike the note and bend up as indicated, then release back to the original note.

COMPOUND BEND & RELEASE: Strike the note and bend up and down in the rhythm indicated.

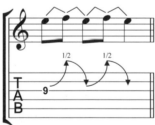

PRE-BEND: Bend the note as indicated, then strike it.

PRE-BEND & RELEASE: Bend the note as indicated. Strike it and release the note back to the original pitch.

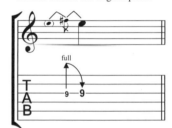

HAMMER-ON: Strike the first note with one finger, then sound the second note (on the same string) with another finger by fretting it without picking.

PULL-OFF: Place both fingers on the note to be sounded, strike the first note and without picking, pull the finger off to sound the second note.

LEGATO SLIDE (GLISS): Strike the first note and then slide the same fret-hand finger up or down to the second note. The second note is not struck.

MUFFLED STRINGS: A percussive sound is produced by laying the first hand across the string(s) without depressing, and striking them with the pick hand.

NATURAL HARMONIC: Strike the note while the fret-hand lightly touches the string directly over the fret indicated.

PICK SCRAPE: The edge of the pick is rubbed down (or up) the string, producing a scratchy sound.

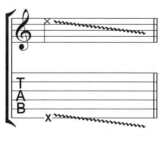

PALM MUTING: The note is partially muted by the pick hand lightly touching the string(s) just before the bridge.

SHIFT SLIDE (GLISS & RESTRIKE) Same as legato slide, except the second note is struck.

6

TAP HARMONIC: The note is fretted normally and a harmonic is produced by tapping or slapping the fret indicated in brackets (which will be twelve frets higher than the fretted note.)

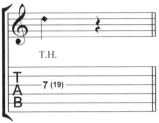

TAPPING: Hammer ('tap') the fret indicated with the pick-hand index or middle finger and pull-off to the note fretted by the fret hand.

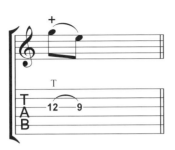

PINCH HARMONIC: The note is fretted normally and a harmonic is produced by adding the edge of the thumb or the tip of the index finger of the pick hand to the normal pick attack.

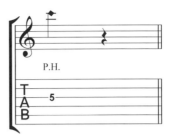

ARTIFICIAL HARMONIC: The note fretted normally and a harmonic is produced by gently resting the pick hand's index finger directly above the indicated fret (in brackets) while plucking the appropriate string.

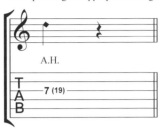

TRILL: Very rapidly alternate between the notes indicated by continuously hammering-on and pulling-off.

RAKE: Drag the pick across the strings with a single motion.

TREMOLO PICKING: The note is picked as rapidly and continuously as possible.

ARPEGGIATE: Play the notes of the chord indicated by quickly rolling them from bottom to top.

SWEEP PICKING: Rhythmic downstroke and/or upstroke motion across the strings.

VIBRATO DIVE BAR AND RETURN: The pitch of the note or chord is dropped a specific number of steps (in rhythm) then returned to the original pitch.

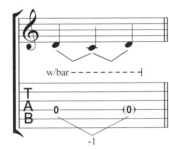

VIBRATO BAR SCOOP: Depress the bar just before striking the note, then quickly release the bar.

VIBRATO BAR DIP: Strike the note and then immediately drop a specific number of steps, then release back to the original pitch.

additional musical definitions

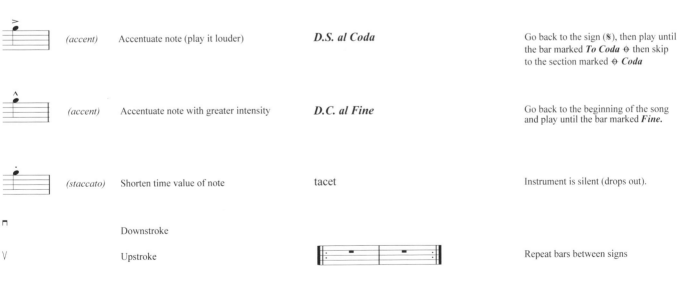

(accent) — Accentuate note (play it louder)

(accent) — Accentuate note with greater intensity

(staccato) — Shorten time value of note

Downstroke

Upstroke

D.S. al Coda — Go back to the sign (𝄋), then play until the bar marked *To Coda* ⊕ then skip to the section marked ⊕ *Coda*

D.C. al Fine — Go back to the beginning of the song and play until the bar marked *Fine.*

tacet — Instrument is silent (drops out).

Repeat bars between signs

NOTE: Tablature numbers in brackets mean:
1. The note is sustained, but a new articulation (such as hammer-on or slide) begins
2. A note may be fretted but not necessarily played.

When a repeat section has different endings, play the first ending only the first time and the second ending only the second time.

aka... what a life!

Words and Music by
Noel Gallagher

Full performance demo: track 1
Backing only: track 8

8

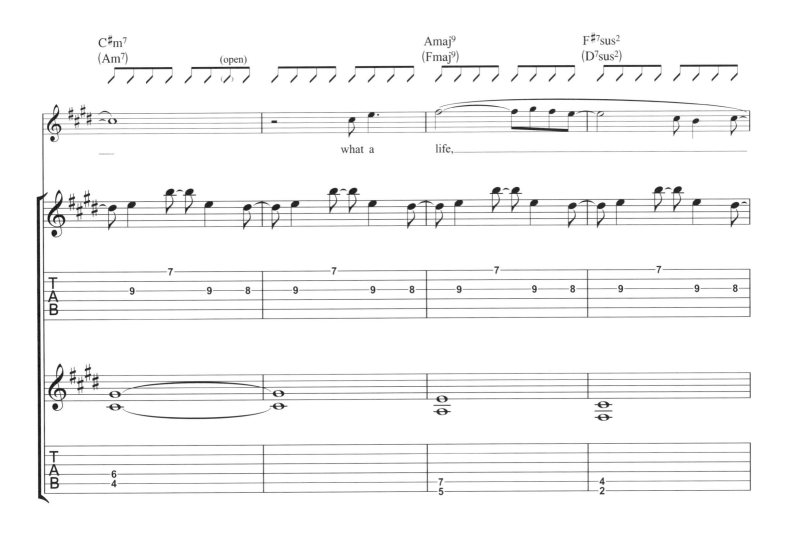

what a　　　　life,

what a　　　　life!

Play Gtr. 3 part

12

Chorus

life,_____ And what a

Gtr. 3 plays Fig. 2

life!_____

Play Gtr. 2 part

Outro verse

Piano plays Fig. 1
Gtr. 3 tacet

Some day_ you_ might find_ your he - ro,_

some say_ you_ might lose_ your mind. Woo - hoo,

Woo - hoo._____ Woo - hoo,

can't stand me now

Words and Music by
Pete Doherty, Carl Barat & Mark Myers

Full performance demo: track 2
Backing only: track 9

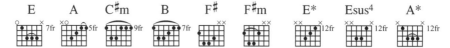

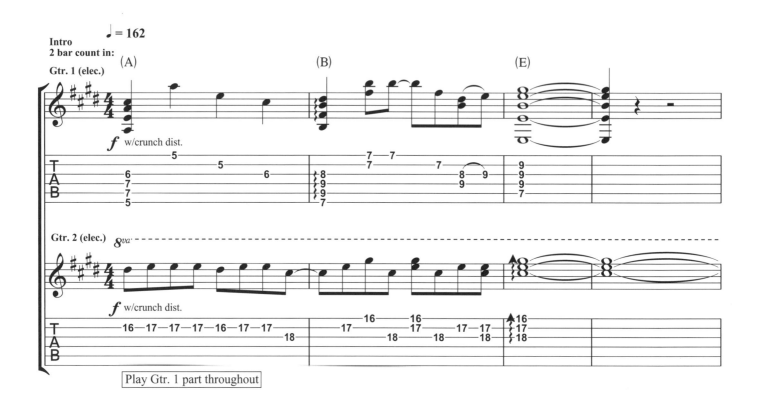

Play Gtr. 1 part throughout

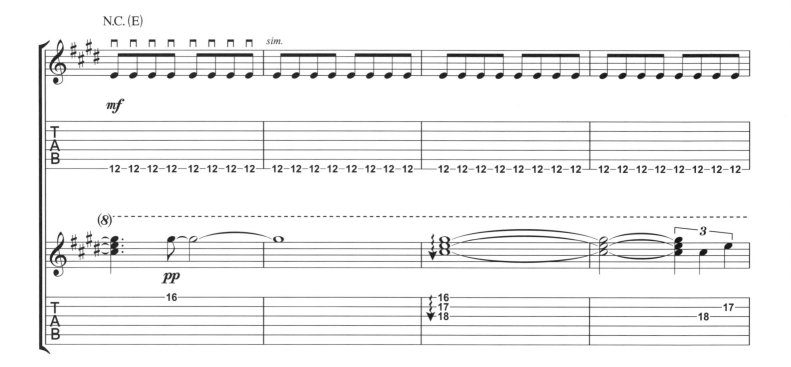

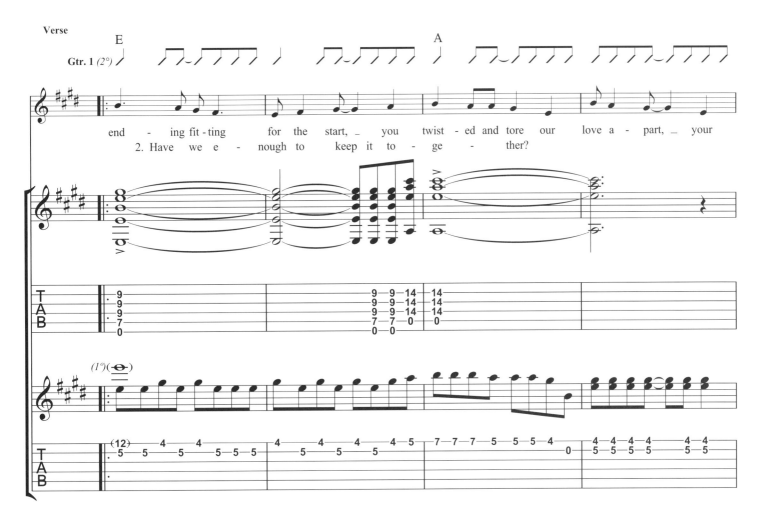

end - ing fit - ting for the start, _ you twist - ed and tore our love a - part, _ your
2. Have we e - nough to keep it to - ge - ther?

let ring…

light fin - gers through the dark __ shat - tered the lamp _ in - to dark - ness, they cast _ us all.
(And you
Or do we just keep on pre - tend - ing, and hope our luck is nev - er end - ing oh.

know you've got it the wrong way round, __ you shot me up __ and blamed it on __ the brown.
You tried to pull the wool, I was-n't feel-ing too cle-ver. And you

__ Cor-nered the boy, kicked out at the world, the world kicked back a lot fuck-ing hard-er now.)
take all that they're lend-ing un-til you need a-mend-ing now.

18

19

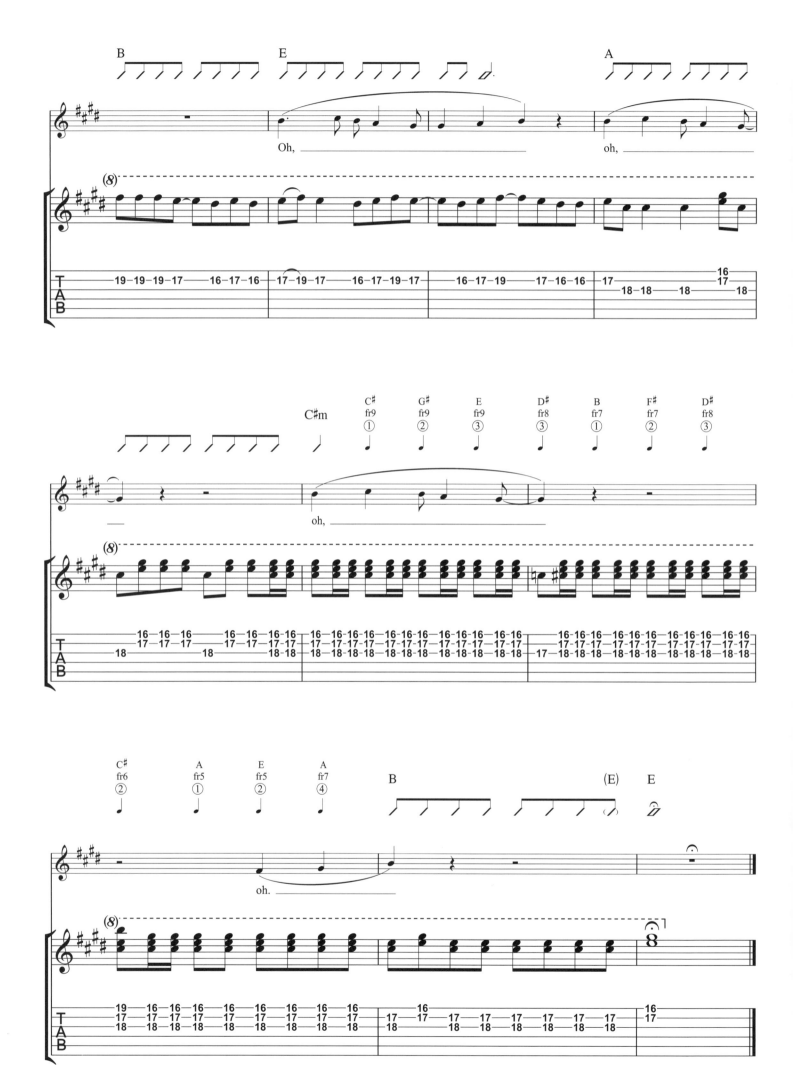

ruby

Words and Music by
Nicholas Hodgson, Richard Wilson, Andrew White, James Rix & Nicholas Baines

Full performance demo: track 3
Backing only: track 10

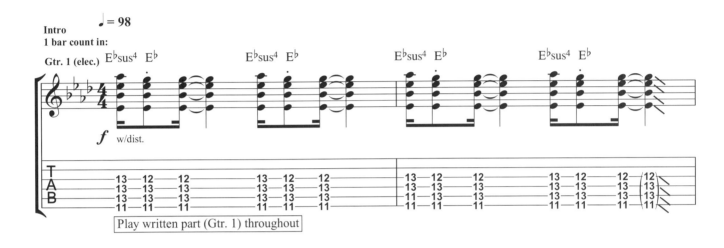

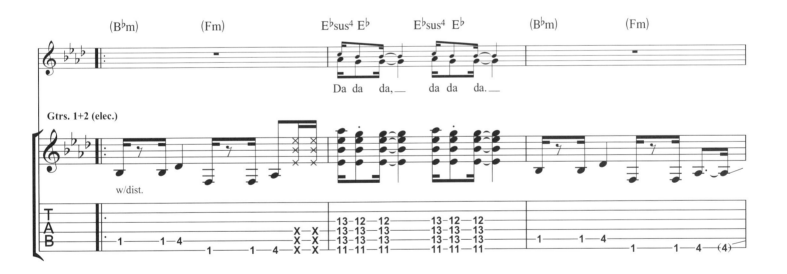

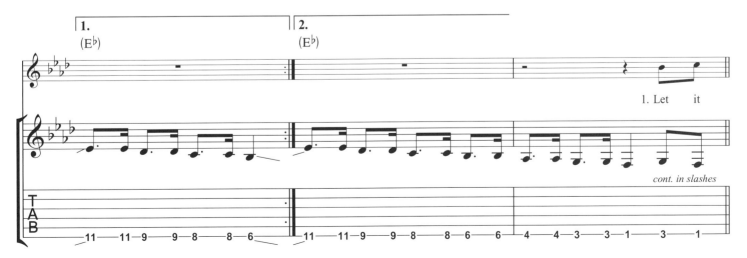

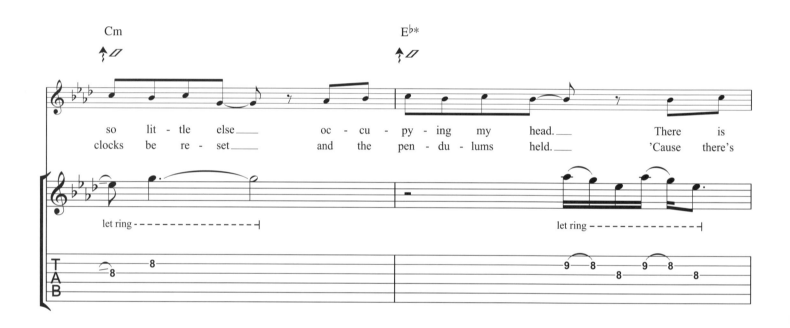

not real - ly fussed,___ does - n't mat - ter to me.___
out what you're called,___ and re - peat - ing your name.___

Ru - by, Ru - by, Ru - by, Ru - by.___ (Ah - ah - ah - ah - ah -

*Gtrs. 1+2

*composite part

- ah.)___ And do ya, do ya, do ya, do ya,___ (Ah - ah - ah - ah - ah -

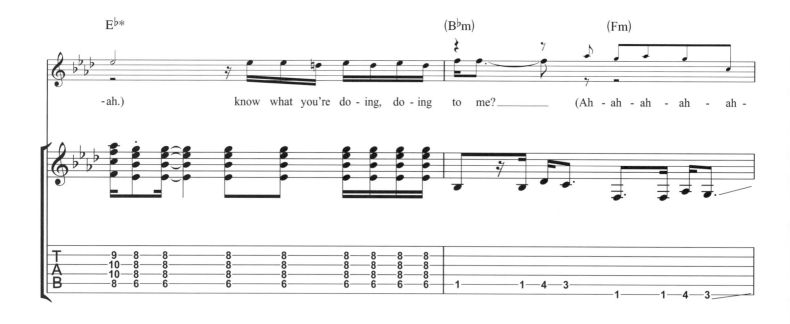

-ah.)   know what you're do-ing, do-ing to me?_____ (Ah - ah - ah - ah - ah-

To Coda ⊕

-ah.)   Ru - by, Ru - by, Ru - by, Ru - by._____ (Ah - ah - ah - ah - ah-

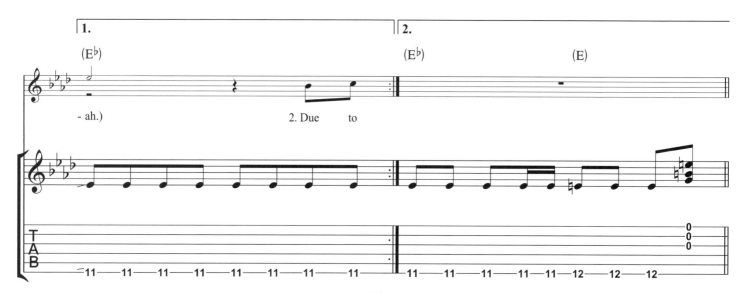

-ah.)   2. Due to

Bridge

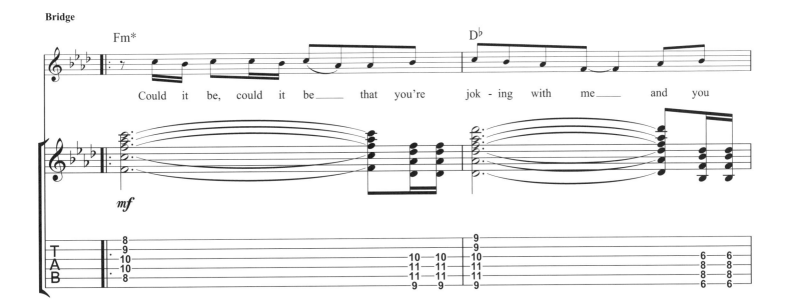

Could it be, could it be___ that you're jok-ing with me___ and you

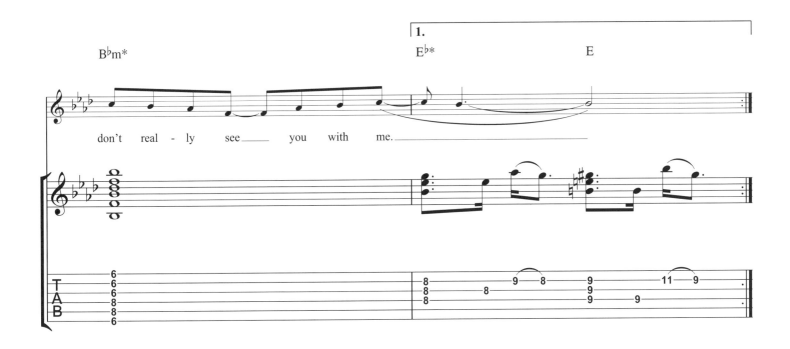

don't real - ly see___ you with me.___

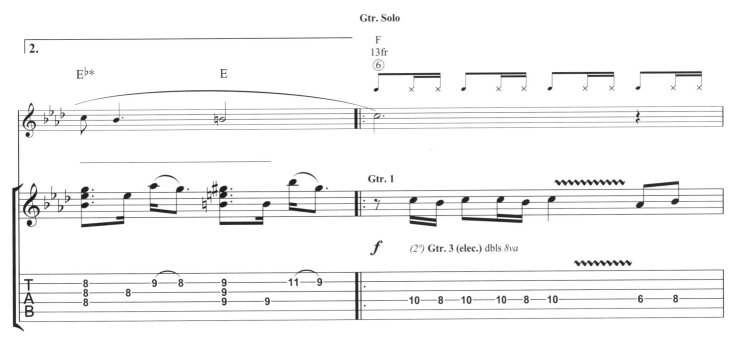

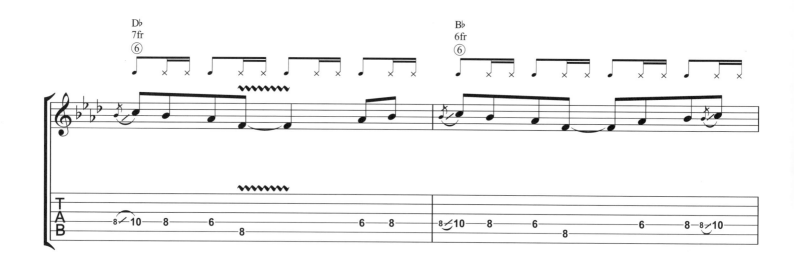

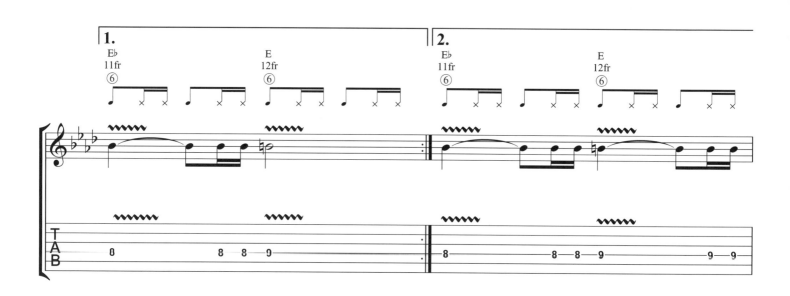

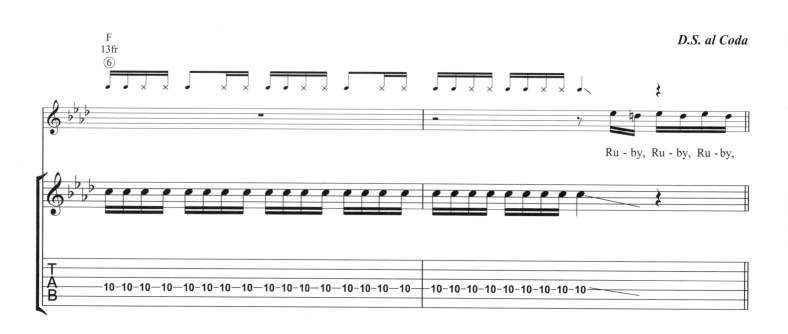

Ru - by, Ru - by, Ru - by,

D.S. al Coda

28

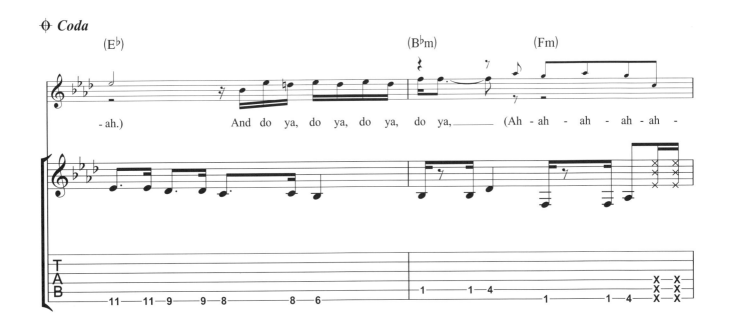

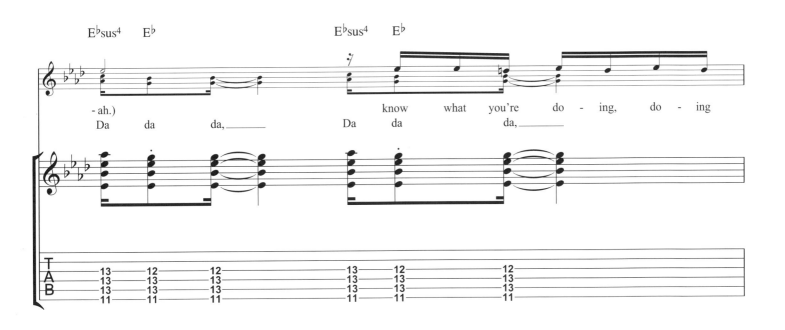

don't sit down 'cause i've moved your chair

Words and Music by
Alex Turner

Full performance demo: track 4
Backing only: track 11

in-to bus-'ness with a griz-zly bear,_____
cir-cu-lar hole with a peg that's square,_____
the Ma-ca-re-na in the de-vil's lair,_____

but just don't_____

To Coda ⊕ | 1.

___ sit down 'cause I've moved your chair._____

f

Gtr. 2 (elec.) (Tune bottom string to D)

w/heavy dist. +
feedback fx

f

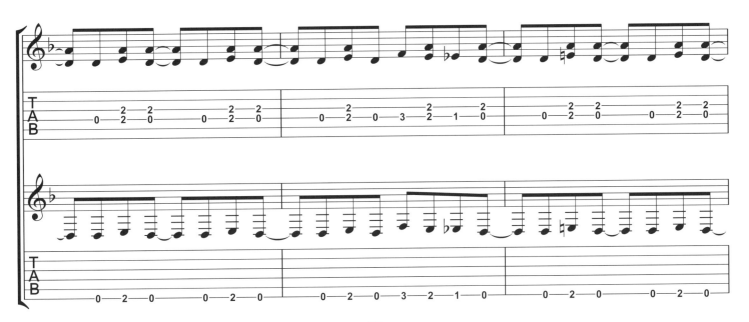

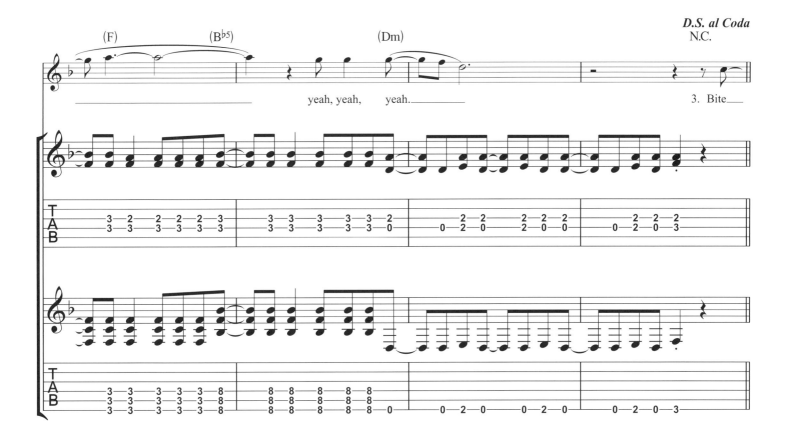

yeah, yeah,   yeah.___   3. Bite___

Chorus

Ooh,___   yeah, yeah,   yeah.___

Gtr. 1

Gtr. 2

Gtrs. 3+4 *(2°)*

Outro

little lion man

Words and Music by
Mumford & Sons

Full performance demo: track 5
Backing only: track 12

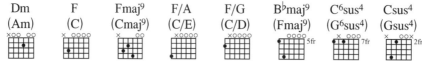

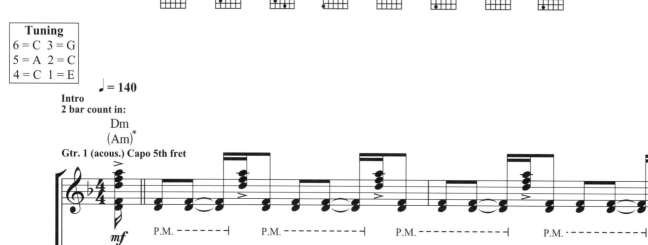

*Symbols in parentheses represent chord names respective to Gtr. 1. Symbols above represent actual sounding chords. Tab 0 = 5fr

Play written part throughout

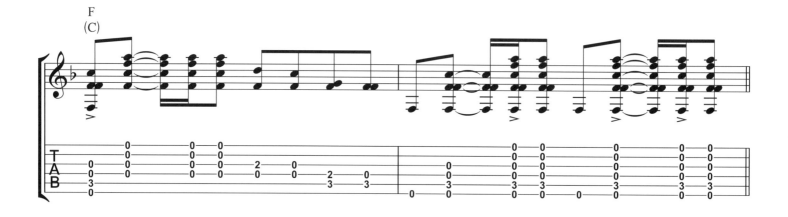

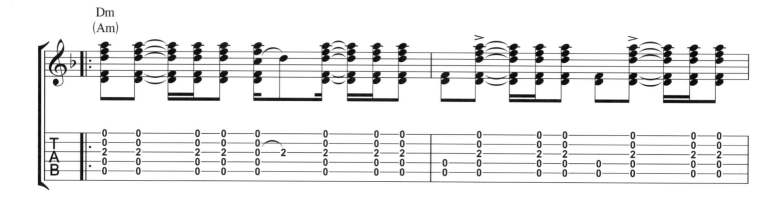

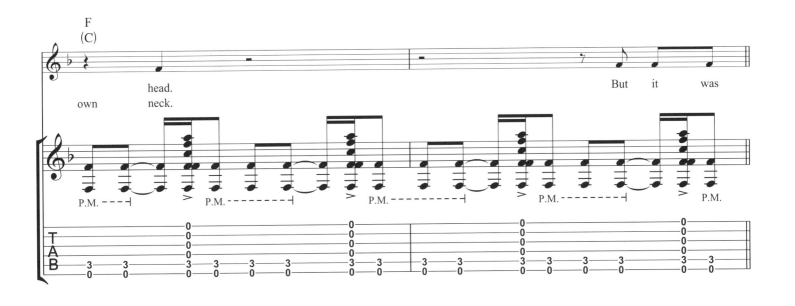

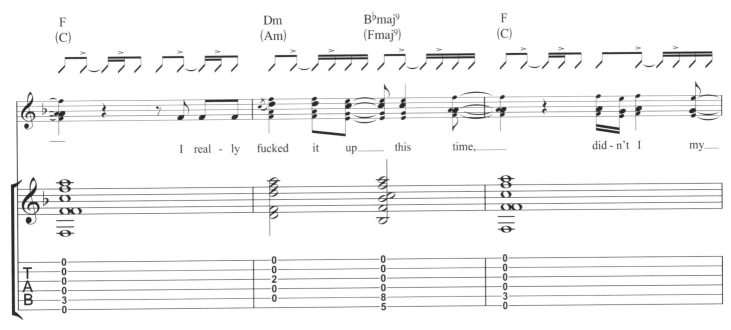

Outro Chorus

run

Words and Music by
Gary Lightbody, Jonathan Quinn, Mark McClelland, Nathan Connolly & Iain Archer

Full performance demo: track 6
Backing only: track 13

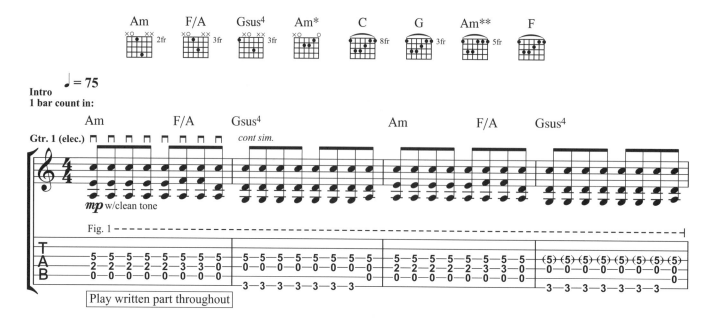

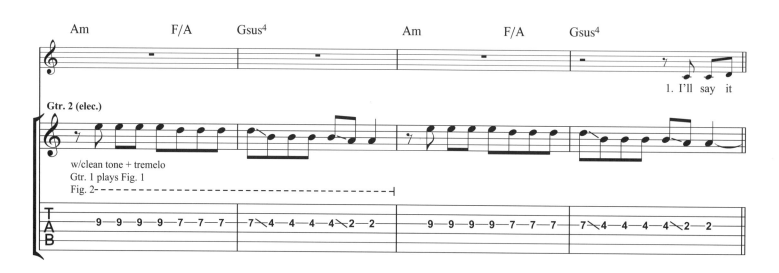

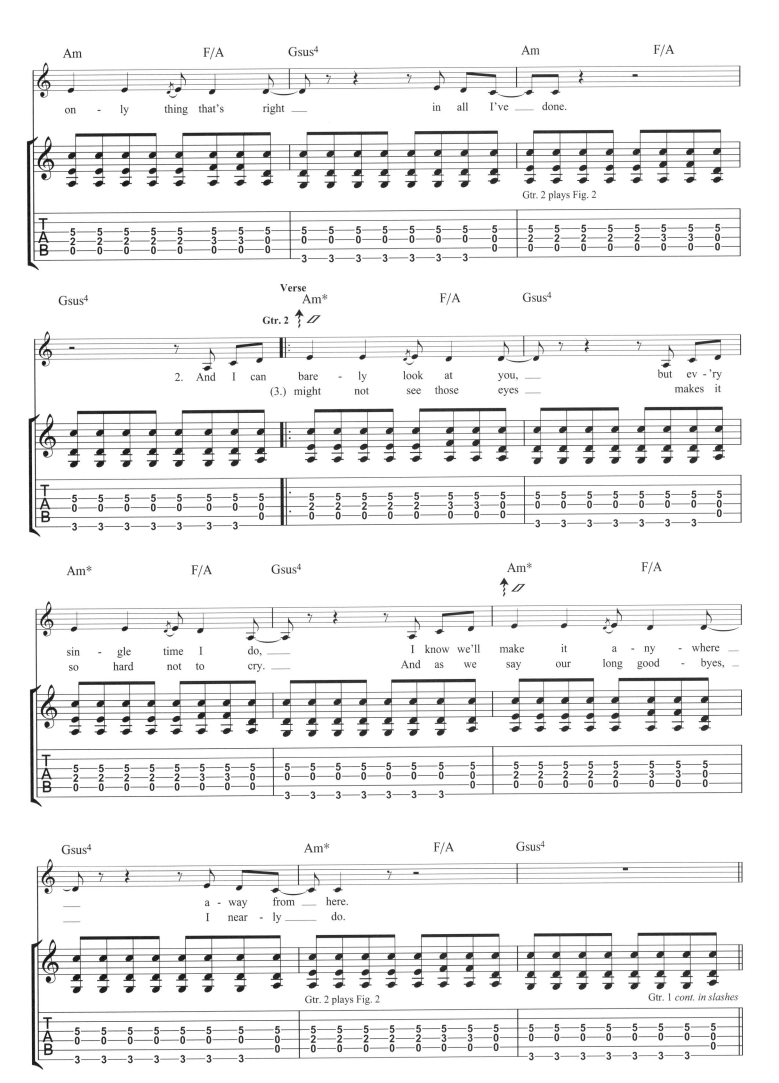

Chorus

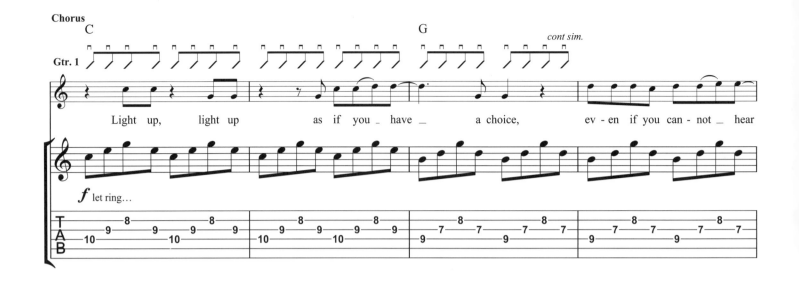

Light up, light up as if you _ have _ a choice, ev - en if you can - not _ hear

f let ring...

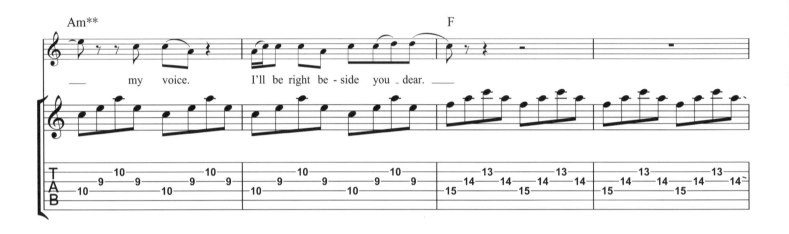

_ my voice. I'll be right be - side you _ dear. _

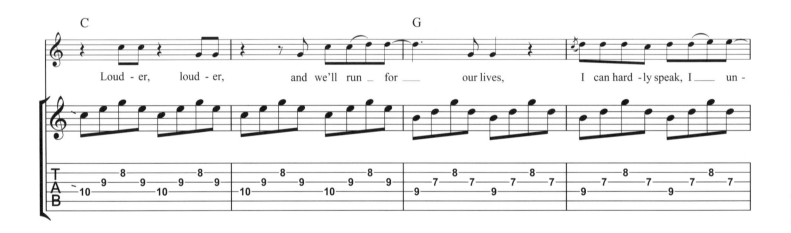

Loud - er, loud - er, and we'll run _ for _ our lives, I can hard - ly speak, I _ un -

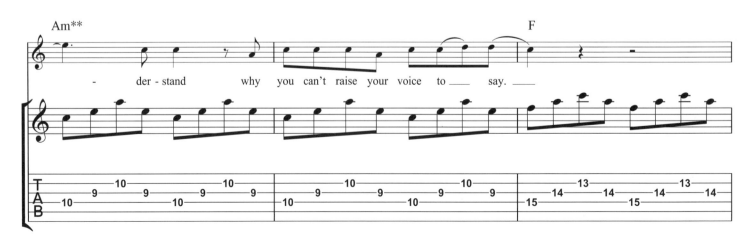

- der - stand why you can't raise your voice to _ say. _

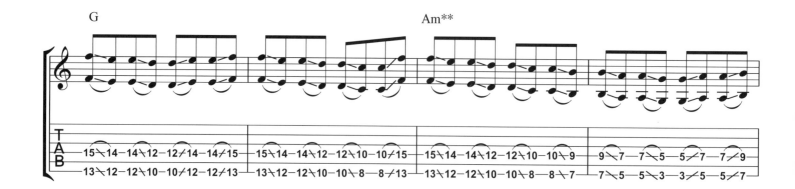

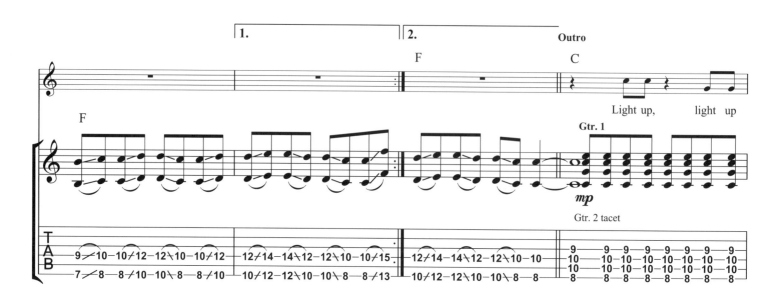

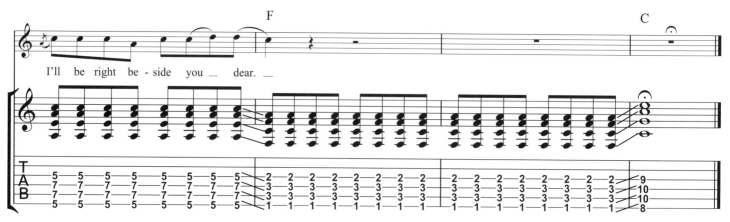

sex on fire

Words and Music by
Caleb Followill, Nathan Followill, Jared Followill & Matthew Followill

Full performance demo: track 7
Backing only: track 14

2. The dark of the al -   Con -sumed

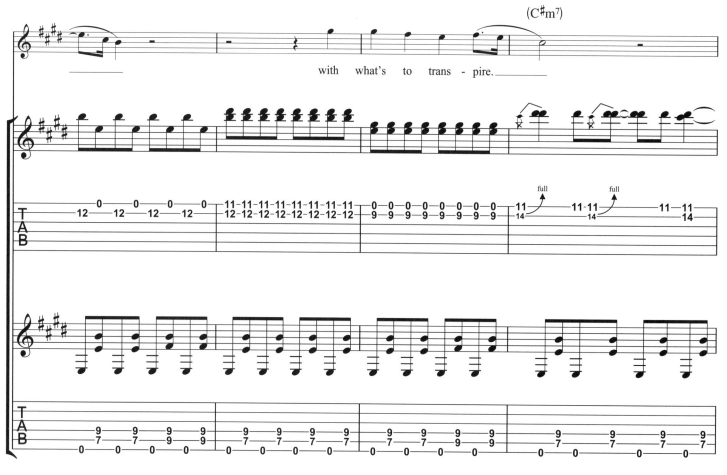

with   what's   to   trans - pire.

with   what's   to   trans - pire.

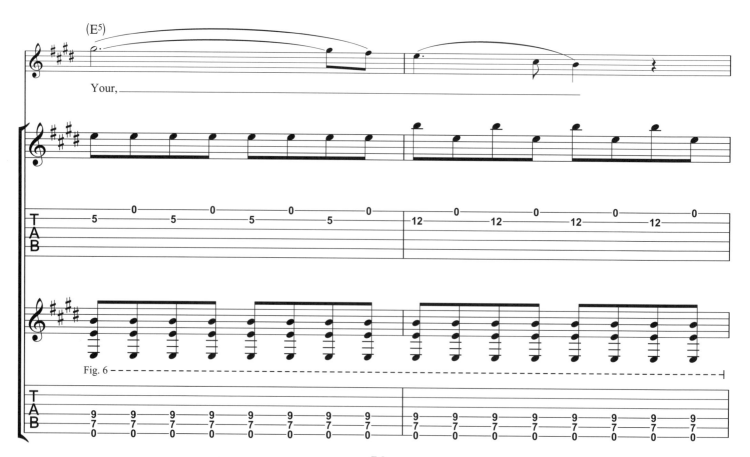

Your,

your sex is on fire.

Con - cerned

with what's to trans - pire.

123456789

CD track listing

Full instrumental performances (with guitar)...

1 **aka... what a life!**
   (Gallagher) Sony/ATV Music Publishing (UK) Limited.

2 **can't stand me now**
   (Barat/Doherty/Myers) EMI Music Publishing Ltd.

3 **ruby**
   (Baines/Hodgson/Rix/White/Wilson) Imagem Songs Limited.

4 **don't sit down 'cause i've moved your chair**
   (Turner) EMI Music Publishing Ltd.

5 **little lion man**
   (Mumford & Sons) Universal Music Publishing Limited.

6 **run**
   (Archer/Connolly/Lightbody/McClelland/Quinn)
   Universal Music Publishing Limited/
   Kobalt Music Publishing Limited.

7 **sex on fire**
   (Followill/Followill/Followill/Followill)
   Bug Music (Windswept Account)/Bug Music Ltd./
   Warner/Chappell North America Limited.

Backing tracks (without guitar)...

8 **aka... what a life!**

9 **can't stand me now**

10 **ruby**

11 **don't sit down 'cause i've moved your chair**

12 **little lion man**

13 **run**

14 **sex on fire**

To remove your CD from the plastic sleeve,
lift the small lip to break the perforation.
Replace the disc after use for convenient storage.